THE MUSIC OF
GEORGE GERSHWIN
FOR SAXOPHONE
Arranged by Robin de Smet

Wise Publications
London/New York/Sydney/Cologne

Exclusive Distributors:
Music Sales Limited,
8/9 Frith Street, London W1V 5TZ, England.
Music Sales Pty. Limited,
120 Rothschild Avenue, Rosebery, NSW 2018, Australia.

This book   Copyright 1987 by Wise Publications.
ISBN 0.7119.1330.7
Order No. AM 68479

Designed by Pearce Marchbank Studio.

Compiled and arranged by Robin De Smet.

Music Sales complete catalogue lists thousands of titles and is free from
your local music book shop, or direct from Music Sales Limited.
Please send £1 in stamps for postage to Music Sales Limited,
8/9 Frith Street, London W1V 5TZ.

Printed in England by
Halstan & Co. Limited, Amersham, Bucks.

Handwritten annotations:
- BUT NOT FOR ME — *Elvis Costello.*
- EMBRACEABLE YOU — *Oleta Adams.*
- HOW LONG HAS THIS BEEN GOING ON? — *Jon Bon Jovi.*
- I GOT RHYTHM — *Robert Palmer.*
- I'LL BUILD A STAIRWAY TO PARADISE — *Issy van Randwyck*
- IT AIN'T NECESSARILY SO — *Cher*
- THE MAN I LOVE — *Kate Bush*
- RHAPSODY IN BLUE — *Larry Adler.*
- SOMEBODY LOVES ME — *Meat Loaf.*
- SOMEONE TO WATCH OVER ME — *Elton John*

Bess, You Is My Woman

Music by George Gershwin

But Not For Me

Music by George Gershwin

Embraceable You

Music by George Gershwin

Fascinating Rhythm

Music by George Gershwin

An American In Paris

Music by George Gershwin

A Foggy Day

Music by George Gershwin

13

How Long Has This Been Going On?

Music by George Gershwin

I Got Plenty O' Nuttin'

Music by George Gershwin

I Got Rhythm

Music by George Gershwin

I'll Build A Stairway To Paradise

Music by George Gershwin

It Ain't Necessarily So

Music by George Gershwin

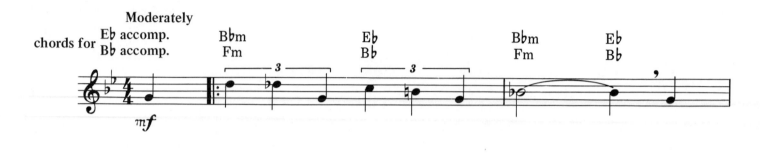

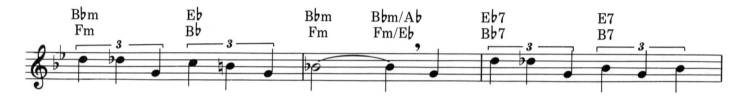

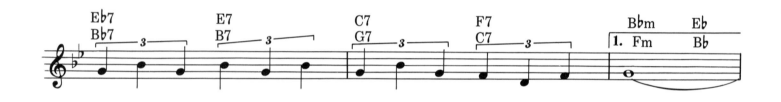

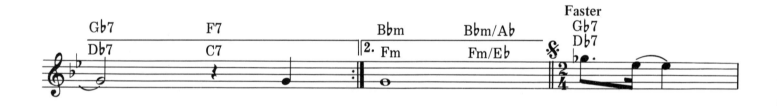

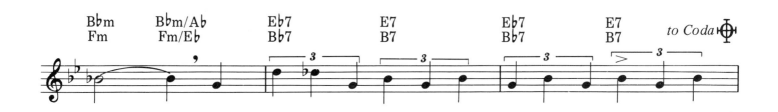

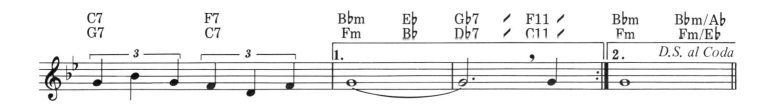

Coda

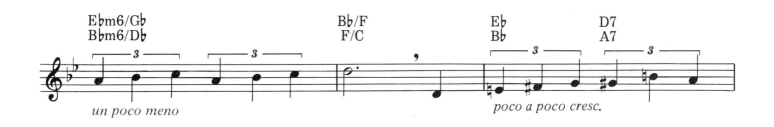

23

Let's Call The Whole Thing Off

Music by George Gershwin

The Man I Love

Music by George Gershwin

Nice Work If You Can Get It

Music by George Gershwin

Oh, Lady Be Good

Music by George Gershwin

Somebody Loves Me

Music by George Gershwin

Someone To Watch Over Me

Music by George Gershwin

Strike Up The Band

Music by George Gershwin

Summertime

Music by George Gershwin

Rhapsody In Blue

Composed by George Gershwin

Swanee

Music by George Gershwin

's Wonderful

Music by George Gershwin

They All Laughed

Music by George Gershwin

45

They Can't Take That Away From Me

Music by George Gershwin